Pickle was a little kitten.

She had soft brown fur and big green eyes.

Sometimes she was a good little kitten and sometimes she was not so good.

One night Pickle and her friend Ginger went into the garden.

Pickle and Ginger saw a hedgehog.

The hedgehog tried to hide.

But the kittens said, 'Peek-a-boo!'

We can see you.

Next, Pickle and Ginger saw a fox.

The fox tried to hide.

But the kittens said, 'Peek-a-boo!'

Next, Pickle and Ginger saw a rabbit.

The rabbit tried to hide.

But the kittens said, 'Peek-a-boo!'

Pickle and Ginger saw an owl.

The owl did not try to hide.

The kittens said, 'We can see you.'

And the owl said, 'I can see you.'

Tu-whit, tu-whoo!